Dang
Mountain

Choose your own adventure

by David Orme

Illustrated by
Paul Savage

For students at Chiltern Tutorial School, Hampshire.

Titles in Full Flight 2

The Bombed House	Jonny Zucker
Gang of Fire	Jonny Zucker
Big Brother @ School	Jillian Powell
Rollercoaster	Jillian Powell
Monster Planet	David Orme
Danger Mountain	David Orme
Goal Scorers	Jonny Zucker
Basketball	Tony Norman
Fight to the Death! A play	Stan Cullimore
Stop Talking at the Back and other poems	(ed.) Jonny Zucker

Badger Publishing Limited
26 Wedgwood Way, Pin Green Industrial Estate, Stevenage,
Hertfordshire SG1 4QF
Telephone: 01438 356907. Fax: 01438 747015.
www.badger-publishing.co.uk enquiries@badger-publishing.co.uk

Danger Mountain ISBN 1 85880 379 9

Series Editor: Jonny Zucker
Publisher: David Jamieson
Editor: Paul Martin
Design: Jain Birchenough
Cover illustration: Paul Savage

Danger Mountain

You are a **brave explorer**. One day, you are looking through an old book when a treasure map falls out of it.

For months, you search the wild and lonely lands looking for the doorway to
DANGER MOUNTAIN.
At last you find it!

But **TAKE CARE**.
The undergound tunnels are full of
DEADLY DANGERS
to stop you reaching the treasure - and none of them are shown on the map!

Open this book to start the adventure -
if you dare!

Badger Publishing

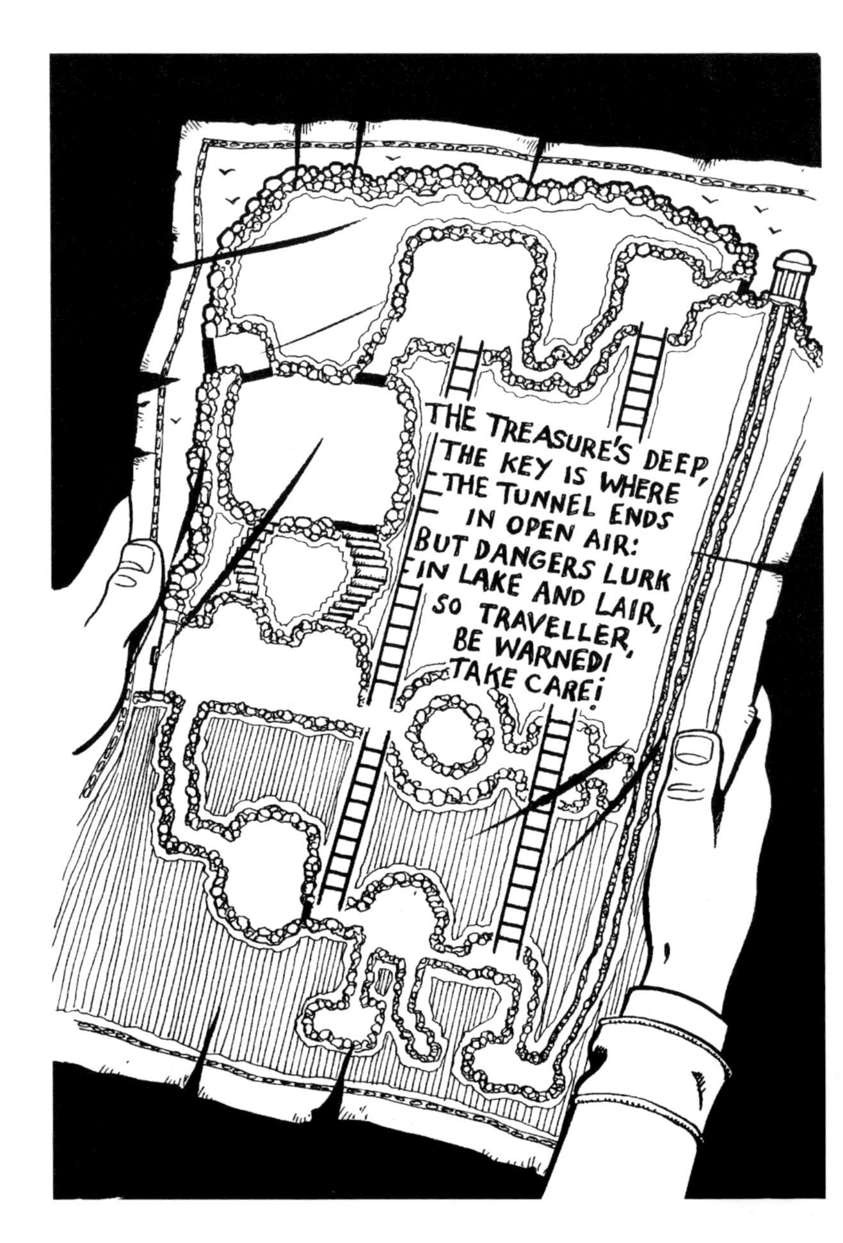
THE TREASURE'S DEEP,
THE KEY IS WHERE
THE TUNNEL ENDS
IN OPEN AIR:
BUT DANGERS LURK
IN LAKE AND LAIR,
SO TRAVELLER,
BE WARNED!
TAKE CARE!

1. In a hidden valley, you find the front door of the mountain! This message is painted on it:

What do you think?

26? GO TO **26**

28? GO TO **28**

11? GO TO **11**

2. You should have thought harder about the riddle! The rope is weak. You are over half way down. It begins to break - strand by strand!

You just reach the bottom as the last strand breaks. You are in a dungeon - with no way out!

Try again? GO TO **1**

3. You are in an underground room. A shaft with a metal ladder in it goes up and down. One way, a tunnel is covered with bright stones. The other way, you see a skeleton. A bony finger is pointing along the tunnel.

Where will you go?

Up the ladder	GO TO **37**
Down the ladder	GO TO **23**
Along the tunnel with bright stones	GO TO **20**
The way the skeleton points?	GO TO **9**

4. You find yourself in the great hall of the mountain kingdom. Here, the kings of old had great feasts, but now there is no sound - except for the clicking of rats' claws. There are three painted doors. What will you find if you open them? You have four choices:

The purple door with **NO ENTRY** on it	GO TO **14**
The small green door	GO TO **10**
The wide yellow door	GO TO **27**
The gloomy stairs covered in cobwebs	GO TO **21**

5. Phew! Luckily, you have chosen the right jar. You swallow the disgusting tasting antidote and throw the empty jar at the spider to distract it while you

GO TO **20**

6. You now have three choices. One way is very smelly, another isn't, and one way is painted green.

Which way will you choose?
The very smelly tunnel? GO TO **29**
The non-smelly tunnel? GO TO **20**
The green tunnel? GO TO **17**

7. This was a really bad idea.
The tunnel suddenly goes steeply down, and you find yourself sliding, sliding... GO TO **24**

8. The tunnel goes down and down. At last you reach a cave filled with deep water. You can see another tunnel on the other side. In the murky deep lives the dreaded fang fish. Do not put your feet or fingers in the water!

Two boats are tied up. Which one will you use to cross the water? Or would you rather go back up the tunnel?

The blue boat?	GO TO **41**
The red boat?	GO TO **30**
Go back up the tunnel?	GO TO **21**

9. You should have ignored the skeleton. A door slams down behind you. You are trapped! On the door there is a poem. It says:

Underneath there are two levers.
Next to one it says **TRESURE**.
Next to the other it says **TREASURE**.

Which one will you pull to open the door?

TRESURE GO TO **42**
TREASURE GO TO **3**

10. The doorway is very low but you manage to get through. Ahead of you, through the door, a narrow tunnel leads up.

Carry on up the tunnel? GO TO **15**
Go back through the door? GO TO **35**

11. You are right! There are eleven letters in THE ALPHABET - count them! The great oak door slowly creaks open. You step inside... GO TO **21**

12. You have not chosen wisely! As you lift the key from its hook, you feel the floor under you opening up. You are falling, sliding into darkness... GO TO **24**

13. One way, a tunnel heads towards an iron door. The other way, the tunnel is black with the soot of many candles. Above you, a rusty ladder goes up into darkness.

Which way will you choose?

Go towards the iron door? GO TO **40**
Climb the rusty ladder? GO TO **17**
Head along the sooty tunnel? GO TO **22**

14. It did say NO ENTRY! This door opens straight onto a high cliff. The sudden sunlight blinds you. You step out. You find yourself falling. Below, the jagged rocks are waiting...

Try again? GO TO **1**

15. You are now in a square room. There are three ways out of it. One tunnel slopes down to a green door. Another tunnel slopes up and you can hear the sound of running water coming from it. In the floor, a rusty ladder is fixed to the side of a dark shaft.

Try the narrow tunnel that slopes down to the green door? GO TO **35**

Take the tunnel that heads up towards the sound of running water? GO TO **18**

Climb down the ladder? GO TO **17**

16. The jar is empty! Slowly, you fall into a deep sleep. The hungry spider comes closer...

Try again? GO TO **1**

17. You are in a damp, narrow tunnel with a shaft in the roof and the floor. Both shafts have rusty ladders in them. In one direction, the tunnel is painted green and is smelly!

Which way will you go?
Along the green tunnel towards the smell? GO TO **6**
Along the tunnel away from the smell? GO TO **36**
Up the rusty ladder? GO TO **15**
Down the rusty ladder? GO TO **13**

18. Water starts to flow along the tunnel. The roof gets lower and lower until it dips under the water.

What will you do?
Go back? GO TO **15**
Dive under the water and hope that you can reach the tunnel on the other side before you drown? GO TO **37**

19. Well done! You solved the rhyming riddle. You climb carefully down the rope. It is a long way down, and your arms are very tired.

At the bottom is a dark dungeon. In the centre of the dungeon is a huge oak chest, but do you have the key to open the chest? Do you know what jewel is on the handle? You must match the jewel with the padlock!

I haven't found the key yet GO TO **33**

Yes! I have already found the key:

Open the **diamond** padlock GO TO **32**

Open the **ruby** padlock GO TO **43**

20. You now have three choices. One tunnel is covered with bright stones. Another tunnel is very smelly. The third tunnel isn't smelly at all.

Try the smelly tunnel? GO TO **29**
Try the one with bright stones GO TO **3**
Try the non-smelly tunnel? GO TO **6**

21. You have reached the entrance hall of the mountain kingdom. You have four choices.

Go out through the great front door GO TO **25**
Climb a set of gloomy stairs covered in cobwebs GO TO **4**
Walk along a wide tunnel with old flags in it GO TO **36**
Take a narrow, twisting tunnel that goes downwards GO TO **8**

22. You have reached a round room. Two shafts go down. One has a white rope, the other a black rope. In one direction, there is a sooty tunnel. The other way, there is a tunnel so low you will have to crawl along.

On the wall, a riddle is painted:

Which is the best way to go?

Down the white rope?	GO TO **19**
Down the black rope?	GO TO **2**
Down the sooty tunnel?	GO TO **13**
Crawl along the low tunnel?	GO TO **23**

23. At this point, a metal ladder goes up a shaft. In one way, the tunnel is so low you will have to crawl along. In the other direction, you can feel warm air.

Which way will you go?

Up the shaft?	GO TO **3**
Along the very low tunnel?	GO TO **22**
Towards the warm air?	GO TO **7**

24. ...into a cauldron of boiling lava!

Try again?	GO TO **1**

25. The great door has a handle on the inside, so it is easy to open. You are back in the secret valley, but have you got the treasure?

If you haven't, and you would like another go GO TO **1**

If you have GO TO **44**

26. Most people say this, but it is the wrong answer! A hole above the door opens, and a stream of freezing cold water pours over your head. Deep inside the mountain, you hear a deep, booming laugh...

Try again? GO TO **1**

27. A set of grand stairs sweep down.

Carry on down the stairs? GO TO **36**
Go back into the great hall? GO TO **4**

28. Sorry, that's wrong. The door will not open.

Try again? GO TO **1**

29. This was not a good choice! You have walked into the lair of a giant spider. The spider leaps out and injects you with its deadly venom.

Gasping for breath, you see three stone jars with the word ANTIDOTE painted on them. They are different colours. You only have time to open one jar. One has the antidote in it, but the other two are empty!

Which jar will you choose?

The tall black jar? GO TO **38**
The heavy brown jar? GO TO **5**
The cracked green jar? GO TO **16**

30. Bad idea! The bright red colour has annoyed the dreaded fang fish. It swims to the surface and turns your boat over. Its huge jaws are waiting...

Try again? GO TO **1**

31. You chose well! You now have the key to the treasure. But the treasure is in the deepest part of the mountain, and will not be easy to find - unless, of course, you have already found it!

Carrying the key, turn and

GO BACK TO **37**

32. You open the chest with the key. Inside, you find a huge diamond. This is the treasure of the mountain!

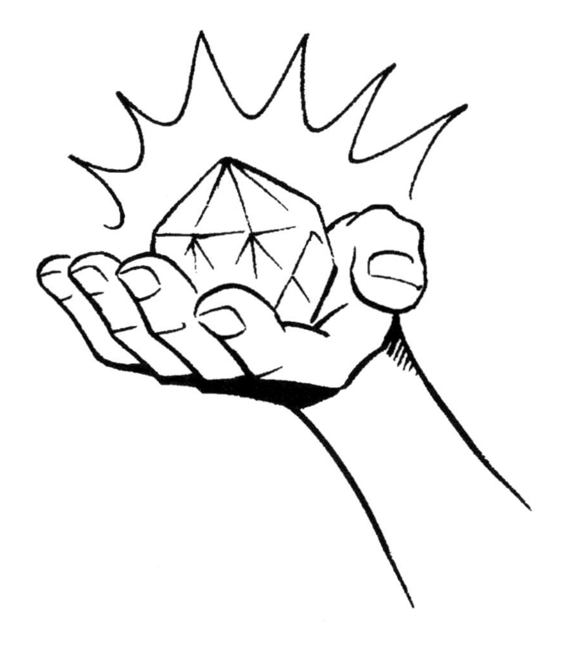

Carefully, you put it in your pocket and start to climb back up the white rope. Now, can you find your way back out of the mountain? GO TO **22**

33. The chest is too heavy to carry up the rope! You will need the key, which is at the very top the mountain. Go back up the white rope to begin your search. GO TO **22**

34. Water starts to flow along the tunnel. The roof gets lower and lower until it dips under the water.

What will you do?

Go back? GO TO **37**

Dive under the water and hope that you can reach the tunnel on the other side before you drown? GO TO **15**

35. You try to open the green door but it won't - this door only opens one way! You have only one choice - GO TO **15**

36. The tunnel widens out into a room. To one side grand stairs go up to a wide, yellow door. One way, the tunnel is narrow and damp. The other way it is wider and has old flags hanging in it.

Which way will you go from this room?

Along the wide tunnel with old flags? GO TO **21**

Up the grand stairs and through the yellow door? GO TO **4**

Along the narrow tunnel? GO TO **17**

37. You have arrived at another underground room. A metal ladder goes down into the darkness. From one tunnel, you hear the sound of running water. From another tunnel, a light flickers. You must choose your way!

Go down the ladder? GO TO **3**

Go towards the sound of water? GO TO **34**

Go towards the light? GO TO **39**

38. The jar is empty! Slowly, you fall into a deep sleep. The hungry spider comes closer...

Try again? GO TO **1**

39. You have reached the very top of the mountain. Ahead of you is a marble temple. On the wall of the temple are two keys. One is gold, with a ruby on it, the other is iron, with a diamond on it. One of them is the key to the treasure - the other one isn't!

There is a riddle painted on the wall.
It says:

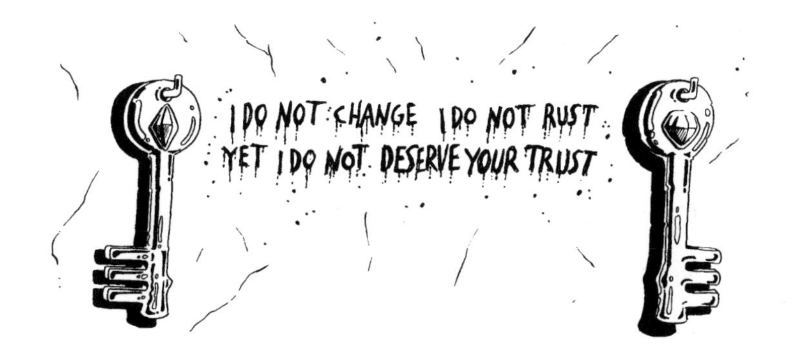

Which key will you choose?

The gold key?	GO TO **12**
The iron key?	GO TO **31**

40. The iron door will not open this way. GO BACK TO **13**

41. This was a good choice. You paddle quietly across the cavern and reach a tunnel on the other side. The tunnel has an iron door in it. What do you do?

Go through the iron door? GO TO **13**

Get back in the boat and go back? GO TO **21**

42. Sorry, wrong lever!
You are trapped for ever!
Try again? GO TO **1**

43. Sorry, wrong padlock. The guardian of the treasure has heard you, and he's much bigger than you...

Try again? GO TO **1**

44. Congratulations! You have escaped with your life, and the treasure!

Prepare for a life of luxury!

THE END